It's Easy To Play Coldplay.

Published by
Wise Publications
14/15 Berners Street, London W1T 3LJ

Exclusive Distributors:
Music Sales Limited
Distribution Centre, Newmarket Road, Bury St. Edmunds, Suffolk IP33 3YB, England.
Music Sales Pty Limited
120 Rothschild Avenue, Rosebery, NSW 2018, Australia.

Order No. AM977801
ISBN 1-84449-139-0
This book © Copyright 2003 by Wise Publications.

Music arranged by Jack Long.
Music processed by Paul Ewers Music Design.
Cover photograph courtesy London Features International.
Printed in the United Kingdom by Caligraving Limited, Thetford, Norfolk.

Your Guarantee of Quality
As publishers, we strive to produce every book to the highest commercial standards.
The music has been freshly engraved and the book has been carefully designed to
minimise awkward page turns and to make playing from it a real pleasure.
Particular care has been given to specifying acid-free, neutral-sized paper made from
pulps which have not been elemental chlorine bleached.
This pulp is from farmed sustainable forests and was produced with special regard for the environment.
Throughout, the printing and binding have been planned to ensure a sturdy,
attractive publication which should give years of enjoyment.
If your copy fails to meet our high standards, please inform us and we will gladly replace it.

www.musicsales.com

Wise Publications
part of The Music Sales Group

London / New York / Paris / Sydney / Copenhagen / Berlin / Madrid / Tokyo

Amsterdam

Words & Music by Guy Berryman,
Jon Buckland, Will Champion & Chris Martin

1. Come on,___ oh my star is fad - ing, and I _____ swerve

out of con - trol.___ If___ I'd, if I'd on - ly wait - ed,

I'd not be stuck here in this___ hole.___

2. Come___ here, oh my star is fad - ing,___
3. Come___ on, oh my star is fad - ing,___

and I_____ swerve out of con - trol._____
and I_____ see no chance of re - lease._____

Clocks

Words & Music by Guy Berryman,
Jon Buckland, Will Champion & Chris Martin

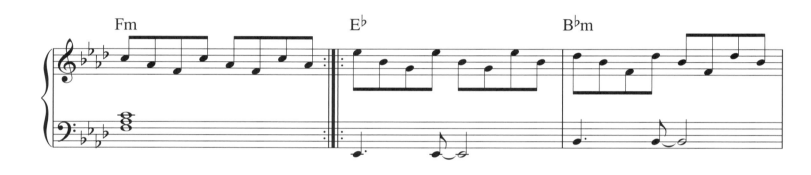

1. The

Don't Panic

Words & Music by Guy Berryman,
Jon Buckland, Will Champion & Chris Martin

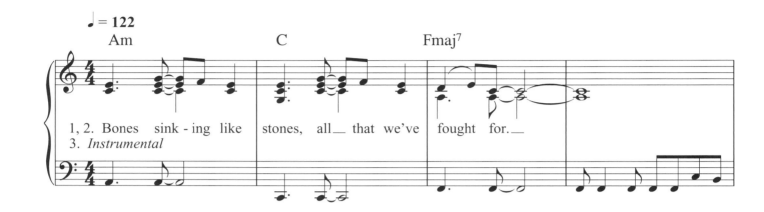

1, 2. Bones sink-ing like stones, all__ that we've fought for.__
3. *Instrumental*

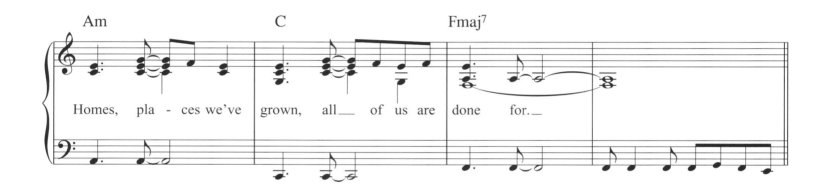

Homes, pla-ces we've grown, all__ of us are done for.__

And we live in a beau-ti-ful world.__ Yeah we do,__ yeah we do.__

__ We live in a beau-ti-ful world.__

Everything's Not Lost

Words & Music by Guy Berryman,
Jon Buckland, Will Champion & Chris Martin

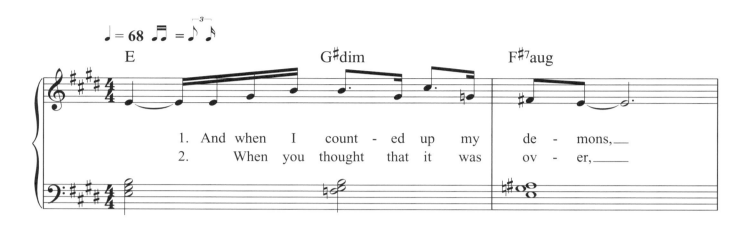

1. And when I count-ed up my de - mons,
2. When you thought that it was ov - er,

saw there was one for ev - 'ry day. ____
you could feel it all a - round. ____

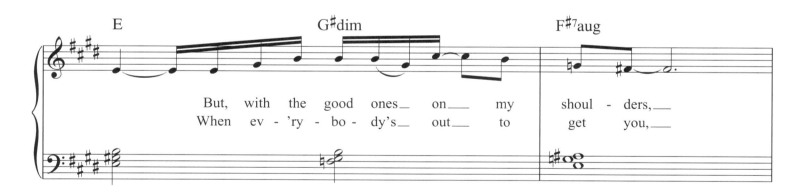

But, with the good ones __ on __ my shoul - ders, ____
When ev - 'ry - bo - dy's __ out __ to get you, ____

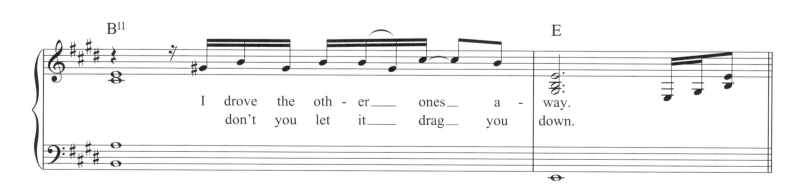

I drove the oth - er __ ones __ a - way.
don't you let it __ drag __ you down.

Green Eyes

Words & Music by Guy Berryman,
Jon Buckland, Will Champion & Chris Martin

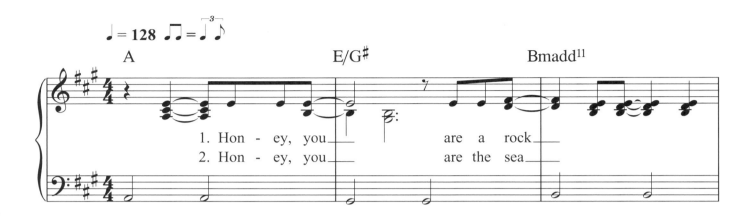

1. Hon - ey, you ___ are a rock ___
2. Hon - ey, you ___ are the sea ___

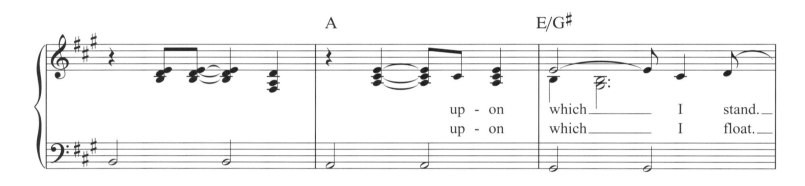

up - on which ___ I stand.
up - on which ___ I float.

And I come ___
And I came ___

here ___ to talk.
here ___ to talk.

In My Place

Words & Music by Guy Berryman,
Jon Buckland, Will Champion & Chris Martin

A Rush Of Blood To The Head

Words & Music by Guy Berryman,
Jon Buckland, Will Champion & Chris Martin

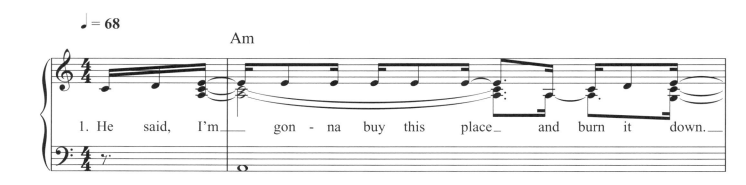

1. He said, I'm gon-na buy this place and burn it down.

I'm gon-na put it six feet un-der-ground.

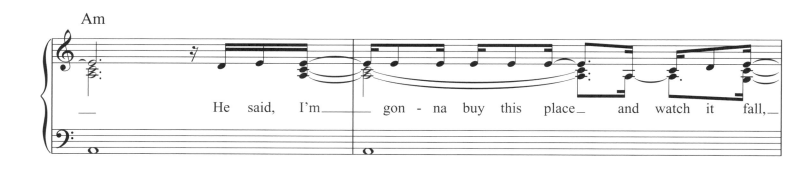

He said, I'm gon-na buy this place and watch it fall,

stand here be-side me, ba-by, in the crumb-ling

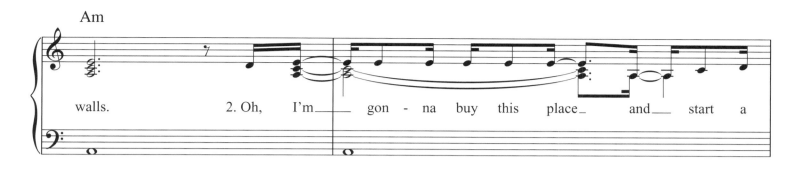

walls. 2. Oh, I'm__ gon - na buy this place__ and__ start a

fire. Stand__ here un - til I fill__ all your heart's de -

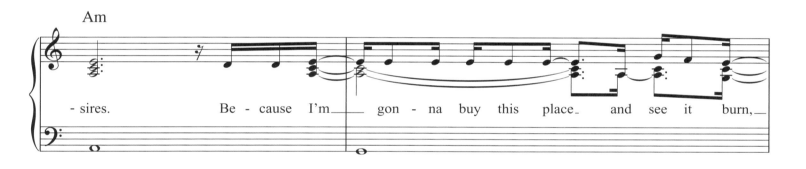

- sires. Be - cause I'm__ gon - na buy this place__ and see it burn,__

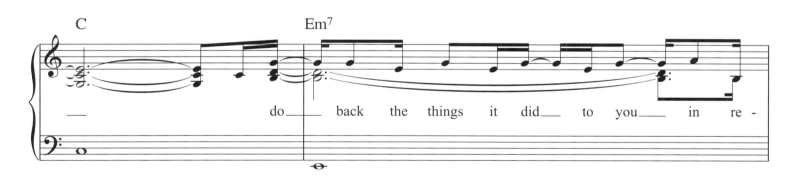

__ do__ back the things it did__ to you__ in re -

- turn._____ Ha,__

C

_ gon - na buy this place_ and see it go._ Stand_

Em⁷

Am

_ here be - side me, ba - by, watch the_ or - ange glow.

C

Some will laugh,_ and some just sit and cry;_ but you_

Em⁷

Am

D.S. al Coda

_ just sit_ down_ there_ and you won - der why._ So I'm_

𝄋 *Coda*

Am

So meet me by_ the bridge,_ oh meet me by_ the lake._

Sparks

Words & Music by Guy Berryman,
Jon Buckland, Will Champion & Chris Martin

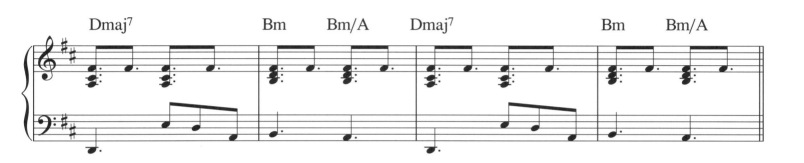

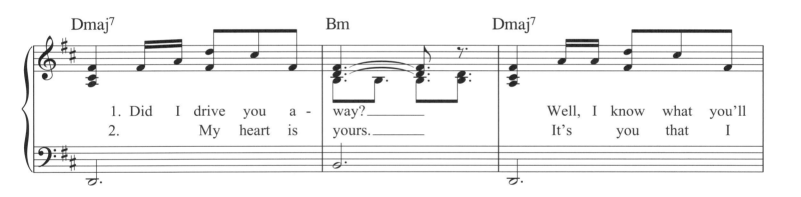

1. Did I drive you a-way?___ Well, I know what you'll
2. My heart is yours.___ It's you that I

say: you'll say___ oh,___ sing one you
hold on to;___ that's what I

The Scientist

Words & Music by Guy Berryman,
Jon Buckland, Will Champion & Chris Martin

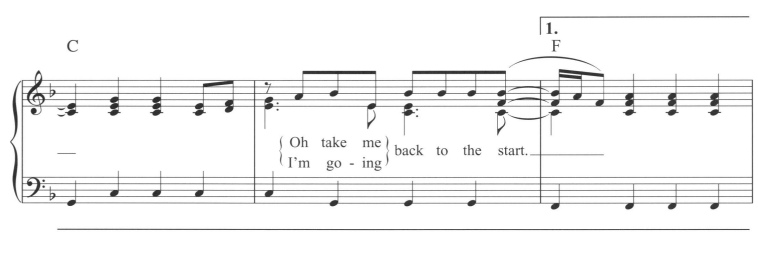

{ Oh take me }
{ I'm go - ing } back to the start.

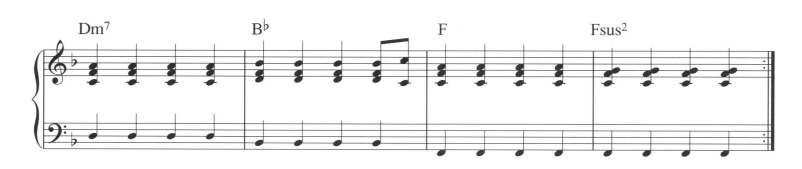

Trouble

Words & Music by Guy Berryman,
Jon Buckland, Will Champion & Chris Martin

thought of all___ the stu - pid things___ I'd said.

2. Oh no, what's
3. Oh no, I

this?   A   spi - der   web,___ and I'm   caught   in the   mid - dle.
see   a   spi - der   web,___ and it's   me   in the   mid - dle.

So I   turned_____ to_____ run,   and
So I   twist_____ and_____ turn,   but

Warning Sign

Words & Music by Guy Berryman,
Jon Buckland, Will Champion & Chris Martin

When the truth is I miss you. Yeah, the truth is that I miss you so.

Yellow

Words & Music by Guy Berryman,
Jon Buckland, Will Champion & Chris Martin

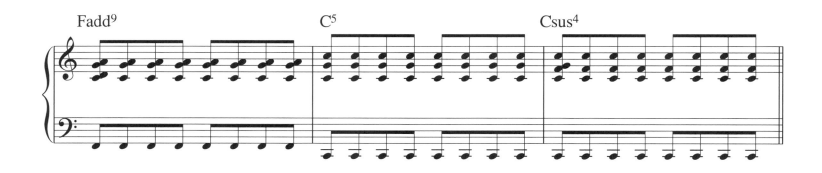

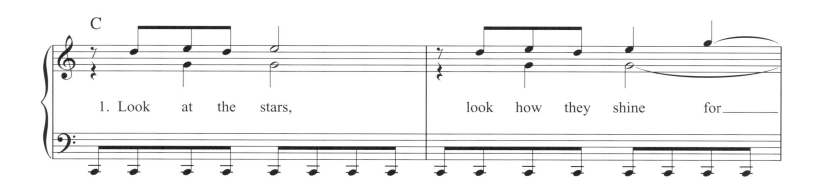

1. Look at the stars, look how they shine for_____

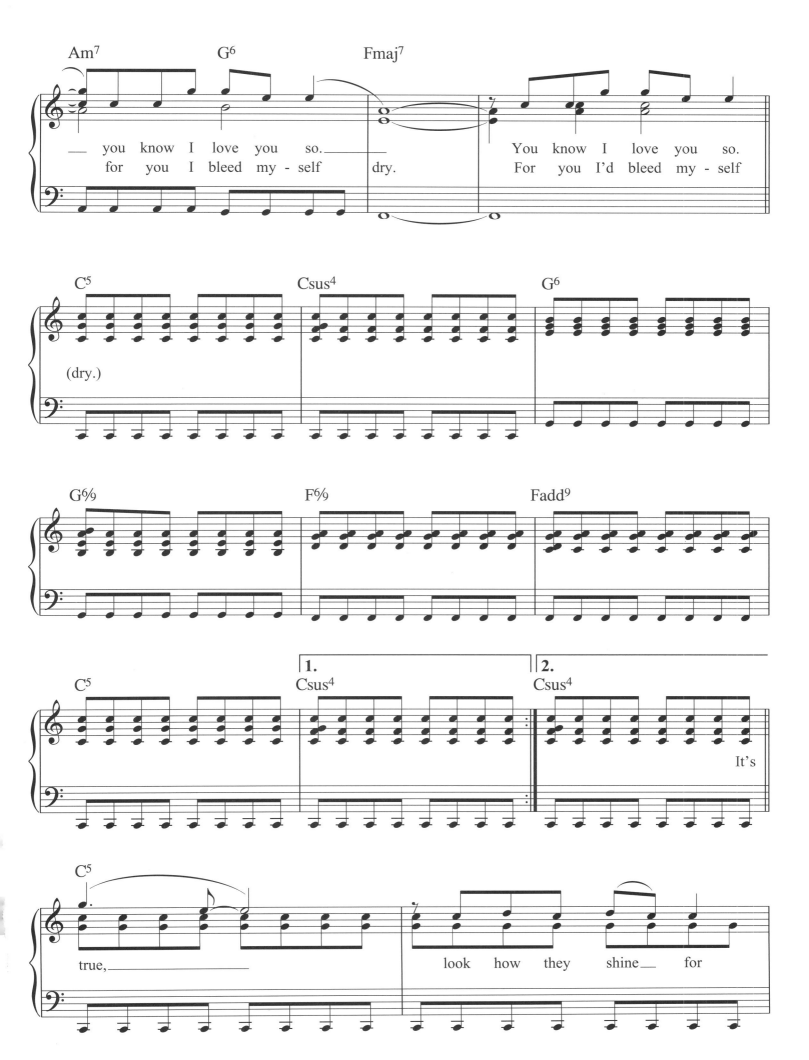

Am⁷   G⁶   Fmaj⁷

you know I love you so.
for you I bleed my-self dry.

You know I love you so.
For you I'd bleed my-self

C⁵   Csus⁴   G⁶

(dry.)

G⁶⁄₉   F⁶⁄₉   Fadd⁹

1.
C⁵   Csus⁴   **2.** Csus⁴

It's

C⁵

true,_____

look how they shine__ for

55